Islands

5

TEST BOOKLET

PEARSON

Contents

Placement	3
Unit 1	6
Unit 2	10
Unit 3	14
Unit 4	18
Unit 5	22
Unit 6	26
Unit 7	30
Unit 8	34
End of term 1	38
End of term 2	40
End of term 3	42
Final	44
Exam preparation	52

1 Read. Then circle.

1 What *make / makes* you happy?   Sunny days *make / makes* me feel happy.

2 Why *are / is* they swimming?   They *am / are* swimming because it's hot.

3 What *is / are* the matter?   I *am / is* tired.

4 *Are / Is* he lazy? No. *I'm / He's* strong and sporty.

2 Read. Then complete.

> ago   now   tomorrow   yesterday

It's Tuesday today. [1] _____ is Wednesday. [2] _____ was
Monday. Sunday was two days [3] _____ . [4] _____ it's
one o'clock. It's lunch time!

3 Read. Then answer.

> Hi. I'm Freddie and it's Friday! Tomorrow it's the weekend. I'm going to go swimming this afternoon and this evening I'm going to play badminton with my friend, Tom. Tomorrow morning, I'm going to play football. My school is going to play in the inter-schools competition tomorrow afternoon. We're fifth. I'm going to go horse riding after the game and then on Sunday I'm going to the beach. I'm going to learn to sail with a friend of mine. Then, on Sunday evening, I'm going to do my homework.

1 What is Freddie going to do after school on Friday afternoon?

_____ .

2 When are Tom and Freddie going to play badminton?

_____ .

3 Is Tom going to play football on Sunday morning?

_____ .

4 When is Tom going to go horse riding?

_____ .

5 What is Tom going to learn to do at the beach?

_____ .

4 Look at this picture. Then circle *True* (T) or *False* (F).

1 The boy on the horse looks worried.   T / F

2 There's a lighthouse.   T / F

3 There's a girl surfing.   T / F

4 There are three boats.   T / F

1 Read. Then match.

1 Did you go to school last Sunday?
2 What does she like doing?
3 Is it Tuesday today?
4 How do you feel?

a I'm excited.
b Rafting and surfing.
c No, I didn't.
d Yes, it's Tuesday.

2 Order to make sentences.

1 walked / school / we / this / to / morning

_____ .

2 football / Saturday / I / on / played / afternoon

_____ .

3 Colombia / three / they / ago / in / lived / years

_____ .

4 is / funny / she / she / jokes / because / tells

_____ .

5 singer / doesn't / be / want / a / she / to

_____ .

3 Read and look. Then complete.

1 I like _____ .

2 She doesn't like _____ .

3 Giraffes eat _____ .

4 Let's go _____ !

4 Write about you.

• What are you like?
• What did you do yesterday?
• What are you doing now?

_____
_____
_____
_____
_____
_____

1 (3:49) **Listen. Then complete.**

doesn't like   evening   TV   problem   running   sitting down   solving   watching

Tony

This is Tony. He's my best friend. He likes [1] _____ problems. Every [2] _____ he solves a different [3] _____ ! He also likes [4] _____ films at the cinema and on the [5] _____ . Tony likes [6] _____ a lot. He isn't very active. He [7] _____ swimming or [8] _____ .

diving   every winter   fast   like   skiing   slowly   swimming

Sue

This is Sue. She's my cousin. She likes [1] _____ and snowboarding. [2] _____ she goes to the mountains with her family. Her mum likes skiing [3] _____. Her dad prefers skiing [4] _____. In the summer they like [5] _____ and [6] _____. They've got a boat and they [7] _____ diving from the boat into the sea.

2 (3:50) **Listen. Then circle.**

Tom: What do you want to do this [1] *evening / afternoon*?

Sam: How about going to the [2] *cinema / theatre*?

Tom: I went to the cinema yesterday. What about listening to [3] *DVDs / CDs*?

Sam: No. I listened to lots of music last night and I [4] *practised / played* the piano all afternoon!

Tom: What about going for a [5] *walk / run*?

Sam: No. I took the dog out this [6] *morning / afternoon* and last night. I'm tired!

Tom: Okay. So ... How about playing [7] *games / chess*?

Sam: That's a good idea. Let's play in the [8] *living / dining* room!

3 (3:51) **Listen. Then write (✓) or (✗).**

1 John and Freddie are friends. ☐

2 John is taller than Freddie. ☐

3 John likes painting. ☐

4 John plays football every day. ☐

5 Freddie wants to be a singer. ☐

6 John wants to be an artist. ☐

7 Freddie has painting lessons on Fridays. ☐

4 **Look. Then talk about the picture. What can you see? What are the people doing?**

5 **Now ask your teacher some questions about the picture.**

6 **What are you going to do today? Tell your teacher.**

1 **Read. Then write.**

Today is Wednesday, October 5th.

1 Tomorrow is _____ .

2 Yesterday was _____ .

3 Two days ago was _____ .

2 **What did Tom do last week? Look. Then write.**

1 <u>On Monday, Tom studied English.</u>

2 _____

3 _____

4 _____

5 _____

Tom's diary

Monday	study English
Tuesday	watch DVD
Wednesday	play tennis
Thursday	go swimming
Friday	go to the cinema

3 **Read. Then complete.**

ago   dark   face   helpful   intelligent   listened   played   problems   studied   today

I have a friend called Bob. He's hardworking and [1] _____ . He always has excellent

results. He's got [2] _____ brown hair and a nice [3] _____ .

It's Saturday [4] _____ and we [5] _____ football this morning

and then [6] _____ to some music. Bob is very [7] _____ .

Sometimes he helps me with my homework. I [8] _____ for a Maths test

two days [9] _____ . I couldn't do one of the [10] _____ so

Bob helped me.

4 **Think of a friend. Then write about him/her.**

• What does he/she look like?

• What is he/she like?

• What did he/she do yesterday?

_____

_____

_____

_____

_____

_____

1 **Read. Then write.**

Today is Sunday, September 1st.

1 Tomorrow is _____ .

2 Yesterday was _____ .

3 Five days ago was _____ .

4 The day before yesterday was _____ .

2 **What did Tina do last week? Look. Then write.**

Tina's diary

1 _____

2 _____

3 _____

4 _____

5 _____

6 _____

7 _____

Monday	study English
Tuesday	watch DVD
Wednesday	chat online
Thursday	go swimming
Friday	have music lessons
Saturday	go running
Sunday	go to the cinema

3 **Read. Then complete.**

ago beautiful shy helped helpful month played practised red spiky sporty tomorrow went

My aunt Rowena is very [1] _____ . She's always doing something! Last weekend,
she [2] _____ tennis with some friends. Last [3] _____ she was skiing in
Switzerland. [4] _____ she's going rock climbing with my uncle George.
She's got [5] _____ [6] _____ hair and is [7] _____ . She's got
a lot of friends and is kind and [8] _____ . At work, she isn't very talkative because
she's very [9] _____ . Two days [10] _____ , I [11] _____ to
my aunt's house and [12] _____ my English words! She [13] _____ me a
lot. I really love my aunt. I want to be just like her!

4 **Think of someone in your family. Then write about him/her.**

- What does he/she look like?
- What is he/she like?
- What did he/she do yesterday?

_____

_____

_____

_____

_____

1 (3:52) **Listen. Then write *True* (T) or *False* (F).**

1 Jo's uncle has got dark brown hair and green eyes.

2 Fred's sister has got long neat hair.

3 Liz's cousin is tall and wears glasses.

4 Ian's aunt is tall and is very pretty.

2 (3:53) **Listen. Then circle.**

1 Her uncle is *lazy / bossy / friendly*.

2 Her sister is *talkative / shy / bossy*.

3 Her cousin is *sporty / talkative / hardworking*.

4 Her aunt is *lazy / shy / sporty*.

3 **Think of the youngest person in your family. Then talk.**

- What does he/she look like?
- Has he/she got ... ?
- What is your ... like?
- Is he/she ... ?
- Is he/she taller/shorter ... than ... ?

© Pearson Education Ltd. 2012

1 **Read. Then listen. Then circle.**

Thomas

I'm [1] *eight / nine*. I've got short brown spiky hair. I've got a lot of friends and I [2] *don't like / like* talking. I'm very talkative. I'm not shy at all. I [3] *like / don't like* homework but I [4] *like / don't like* doing different sports. I play football and basketball and I go swimming [5] *at the weekend / every day*.

Ian

I'm [1] *nine / ten*. I've got short [2] *black / brown* hair and I'm quite good looking. I'm very friendly but my mum says I'm lazy. I [3] *don't like / like* playing on my computer but my mum wants me to help doing the washing up and [4] *cleaning the car / tidying my bedroom*! Ugh. I'm like my dad. He's [5] *lazy / hardworking* but very friendly. Like me!

Georgia

I'm [1] *ten /eleven*. I'm tall and I've got [2] *short / long* brown hair. It's long and straight and always [3] *messy / tidy*. I'm very hardworking and quite clever. I love school work and I love learning about everything. I'm [4] *shy / talkative* with my friends. There's always a lot to talk about. [5] *I'm / I'm not* very sporty. I like reading and I like walking with my dog.

Paula

I'm [1] *eleven / nine*. I'm [2] *short / tall* and quite pretty. I've got short [3] *dark / light* brown hair. It's always messy. I [4] *don't like / love* doing sports. I love swimming, running, ice-skating and rock climbing. I [5] *always / never* watch TV. I've got a lot of friends. They [6] *aren't / are* very sporty. We go ice skating at the weekend. I'm a little [7] *bored / bossy* sometimes. I always want to win and I want everyone to work hard!

2 **Listen. Then circle.**

1 Dad is the *most / more* intelligent in the family.

2 Phil is *more intelligent / less intelligent* than Kate.

3 Charlotte is the *tallest / shortest* in the family.

4 Kate *is / isn't* helpful.

3 **Think of the oldest person in your family. Then talk.**

- What's he/she like?
- Is ... taller/shorter than ... ?
- Are you ... more ... than ... ?

1 **Read. Then match.**

1 take out	**b** my bedroom	**c** my hands	5 meet
2 brush	**d** my homework	**e** my bed	6 do
3 make	**g** my friends	**f** the rubbish	7 tidy
4 wash	**a** for a test	**h** my hair	8 revise

2 **Order to make sentences.**

1 always / my / weekend / I / the / bedroom / tidy / at

_____ .

2 parents / listen / my / should / to / I

_____ .

3 eat / unhealthy / sometimes / food / I

_____ .

4 lunch / my / after / brush / I / teeth / usually

_____ .

5 my / wear / school / must / uniform / I / at

_____ .

6 o'clock / bed / never / ten / I / go / after / to

_____ .

3 **Read. Then give some advice. Use *must* or *should*.**

| eat   go running   go to bed early   study   take your swimsuit   tidy |

1 I've got a test on Friday.   _____ .

2 I'm hungry.   _____ .

3 It's sunny today!   _____ .

4 My room is messy.   _____ .

5 I'm tired.   _____ .

6 I'm going swimming.   _____ .

4 **You've got a test tomorrow. What should you do? Write. Use *should / shouldn't*.**

_____

_____

_____

_____

(1) **Read. Then write.**

1 I make _____ .

2 I do _____ .

3 I revise _____ .

4 I brush _____ .

5 I take out _____ .

6 I wash _____ .

(2) **Order to make sentences.**

1 tidy / at / weekend / the / I / my / bedroom / never

_____ .

2 to / parents / I / listen / always / my

_____ .

3 food / I / healthy / sometimes / eat

_____ .

4 often / I / before / my / lunch / hands / wash

_____ .

5 before / get / school / to / must / half / eight / past / I

_____ .

6 o'clock / bed / should / to / go / I / before / ten

_____ .

(3) **Read. Then give some advice. Use *must* or *should*.**

> have a drink   buy some food   open the window   ask the teacher   study   be on time

1 I'm thirsty.   _____ .

2 I haven't got any lunch.   _____ .

3 I can't do my homework.   _____ .

4 I am always late for school.   _____ .

5 It's hot.   _____ .

6 I've got a test on Friday.   _____ .

(4) **Write about your week. Use *always, never, sometimes ...***

_____

_____

_____

_____

1 **Listen. Then match.**

a messy bedroom

b can't study

c can't sleep

d hasn't got a bin

e tidies on Saturday

Helen

Victor

f listens to quiet music

g eats more healthy food

h eats one vegetable a day

i has pizza one day a week

2 **Listen. Then match.**

1 I always make my bed in the morning ...

2 I never make my bed ...

3 I sometimes wash my face before I go to bed ...

4 I usually do my homework before I watch TV ...

5 I take the dog for a walk with my mum every afternoon after school ...

6 I help my dad wash the car at the weekend ...

a but I never do the washing up!

b and I help my mum take out the rubbish on Tuesday.

c and I always practise my guitar before I do my homework.

d but I always wash my face in the morning.

e before I go to school.

f but I always tidy my room.

3 **Think of healthy food. Then talk.**

- What food is there?
- Where is it?
- You *should*/must always/never ...
- I eat/need ... to ...

1 **Listen. Then match.**

1 I always get bad marks in my tests.

2 I never take notes in class.

3 My mum is ill.

4 Yesterday, I listened to all my CDs. Now I've got nothing to listen to.

a You should help tidy the house and do the shopping.

b You should listen to the radio!

c You should revise!

d You should take notes.

2  **Listen. Then match.**

1 should brush my hair every morning

2 shouldn't eat sweets at playtime

3 should help my sister do her homework

4 must wear my uniform

5 must get to school by 8.30

6 should do my homework every day

7 should clean my teeth before school

8 must eat and drink every day

9 must take my swimsuit to school on Wednesday

10 shouldn't play CDs loudly

3 **Think of unhealthy food. Then talk.**

- What food is there?
- Where is it?
- You should/must always/never ...
- I eat/need ... to ...

1 Read. Then write.

1 I'm good at _____ .

2 I'm _____ .

3 I'm _____ .

4 I'm _____ .

5 I'm _____ .

6 I'm _____ .

2 Reorder to make words. Then match.

1 glypani _____

2 gurninn _____

3 gnignsi _____

4 gwirtin _____

5 gteeinm _____

a friends

b a letter

c karaoke

d the drums

e races

3 Read. Then complete.

| afternoon at last play playing practise prefer singing taking was |

Hi. I'm Jake. I [1] _____ the drums. I like [2] _____ the drums but at the moment, I'm not very good. I'm [3] _____ lessons. I've got a lesson this [4] _____ . I [5] _____ every day. My mum and dad aren't good [6] _____ listening!
[7] _____ Saturday, I [8] _____ playing the drums with my friends. We've got a group. We played for four hours. Paul plays the guitar and Rob sings. Rob's really good at [9] _____ . I [10] _____ playing the drums to doing my homework!

4 What are / aren't you good at? Write.

_____

_____

_____

_____

_____

_____

1 **Read. Then write the question.**

1 _____ ? No, Sam's not good at football.

2 _____ ? Yes, Sue's good at telling jokes.

3 _____ ? Yes, my mum's good at trampolining.

4 _____ ? No, my grandad isn't good at diving.

5 _____ ? I'm good at singing.

2 **Write the question using *good at*. Then circle the answer for you.**

1 _____ ? Yes, I am. / No, I'm not.

2 _____ ? Yes, I am. / No, I'm not.

3 _____ ? Yes, I am. / No, I'm not.

4 _____ ? Yes, I am. / No, I'm not.

5 _____ ? Yes, I am. / No, I'm not.

3 **Read. Then complete.**

at cold don't prefer rather sailing than watching

1 Hi. I'm Molly. I like chess but I'd _____ to be in the school band to the chess club because I'm not very good _____ playing chess.

2 I'm Karen. I'd _____ go rollerblading than read magazines because I like sports.

3 Hi I'm Eric. I'm _____ a programme on TV. I'd rather watch TV than make a snowman because I _____ like _____ weather!

4 Hi, I'm Mark. I love _____ on the sea and I'd rather go sailing _____ diving.

4 **What activities were you doing yesterday? When were you doing them? Write.**

_____
_____
_____
_____
_____

3 Free time

1 🔘 (4:01) **Listen. Then circle.**

1 Bobby's good at …
- **a** telling jokes.
- **b** sport.
- **c** reading books.

2 Sandy's good at …
- **a** playing football.
- **b** reading poetry.
- **c** catching a ball.

3 Charlie isn't good at …
- **a** talking.
- **b** playing the guitar.
- **c** playing tennis.

4 Olivia isn't good at …
- **a** rollerblading.
- **b** reading.
- **c** singing karaoke.

2 🔘 (4:02) **Listen. Then tick (✓) the chart.**

	Betty	Jed	Val	Todd
1 singing karaoke				
2 rollerblading				
3 playing the drums				
4 drawing				

3 **What were you doing last weekend? Make some notes. Then talk.**

1 (4:03) Listen. Then match.

1	at 4 o'clock	**a**	*playing tennis*
2	before school	**b**	*walking home from school!*
3	at the weekend	**c**	*watching a DVD*
4 . yesterday evening		**d**	*finishing homework*
5	at 3 o'clock	**e**	*visiting*
6	at 12 o'clock last night	**f**	*sleeping*

2 (4:04) Listen and circle *True* (T) or *False* (F). Then correct.

1 He was walking home at 3 o'clock.   T / F _____

2 Harry was going to the stadium.   T / F _____

3 Harry went rollerblading and Ben went home.   T / F _____

4 Sue's piano lesson was at half past four.   T / F _____

5 Sue's was practising some difficult music.   T / F _____

6 Sue learns quickly.   T / F _____

3 Think of some games. Make some notes. What would you rather do?

- I'd prefer to ...
- I'd rather ...

1 **Read. Then write.**

volcano

much	many

space

statue

water

pyramid

rainforest

lake

sky

time

air

2 **Write the questions. Then answer.**

1 How many _____ ? (*lake/ Egypt*)

There _____ .

2 How much _____ ? (*air / Mercury*)

There _____ .

3 How many _____ ? (*desert / Italy*)

There _____ .

4 How many _____ ? (*pyramid / Spain*)

There _____ .

5 How much _____ ? (*water / Neptune*)

There _____ .

6 How many _____ ? (*city / China*)

There _____ .

3 **Read. Then write the plural.**

I'm on holiday in Italy. There are lots of towns and [1] _____ (city).
There are some [2] _____ (volcano). There are lots of very old
[3] _____ (statue). In the north of Italy, there are some beautiful
[4] _____ (lake) and [5] _____ (forest).

4 **Write about where you live. Use *some / any*.**

_____

_____

_____

_____

_____

_____

Around the world

Reading and writing B

1 Read. Then write. Write plurals where needed.

space　　environment

much	many

planet　statue

air　city

hill　forest　cave

2 Write the questions and complete the answers. Use *Are there / Is there … ?*

(pyramid / Australia)

1 _____ ?

No, _____ .

(lake / UK)

2 _____ ?

Yes, _____ .

(cave / Spain)

3 _____ ?

Yes, _____ .

(volcano / Mexico)

4 _____ ?

Yes, _____ .

3 Read. Then complete.

In my country there ¹ _____ lots of forests. In the forests there are

² _____ lakes. There ³ _____ any volcanoes but there

⁴ _____ some hills. There ⁵ _____ any deserts.

There's too ⁶ _____ rain! I love my country!

4 Write about a place you like. Use *There is / isn't* and *There are / aren't.*

_____

_____

_____

_____

_____

_____

1 (4:05) **Listen. Then circle.**

1 In Mexico there ...

    a are some volcanoes.
    b aren't any beaches.

2 In Egypt there ...

    a aren't any pyramids.
    b are some pyramids.

3 In Australia there ...

    a isn't a rainforest.
    b are some deserts.

4 In Canada there ...

    a are some forests.
    b isn't a rainforest.

5 In Ireland there ...

    a aren't any lakes.
    b are some forests.

6 In the UK there ...

    a aren't any old forests.
    b are some old forests.

2 (4:06) **Listen. Then circle *True* (T) or *False* (F).**

1	Eliza is from Brazil.	T / F
	There are many rainforests in Brazil.	T / F
	It never rains in Brazil.	T / F
2	Some of Mount Everest is in China.	T / F
	There aren't many rivers in China.	T / F
	The Yangtze is the name of a mountain.	T / F
3	Monika is from Europe.	T / F
	There aren't any lakes in Poland.	T / F
	There are some bears in the forests.	T / F
4	There are some high mountains in Greece.	T / F
	There aren't any islands.	T / F
	There aren't any old buildings.	T / F

3 **Talk about our planet. Make some notes.**

- How many ... are there?
- Is there any ... ?
- How much ... is there?
- Are there any ... ?

© Pearson Education Ltd. 2012

1 🔊 4:07 **Listen. Then match.**

1	Argentina	**a**	mountain lakes
2	Greece	**b**	beautiful beaches
3	Australia	**c**	volcanoes
4	Colombia	**d**	forests
5	Italy	**e**	beautiful lakes

2 🔊 4:08 **Listen. Then circle *True* (T) or *False* (F).**

1	Argentina is in North America.	T / F
2	Some mountains have snow on them in winter.	T / F
3	The grasslands are in the middle.	T / F
4	There aren't many farms in Argentina.	T / F
5	La Boca is the name of a river in Argentina.	T / F
6	There are some volcanoes in Argentina.	T / F

3 **Talk about the environment in your country. Make some notes.**

- How many ... are there?
- How much ... is there?
- Is there any ... ?
- Are there any ... ?

1 **Read. Then write.**

  1 sixty   _____

  2 a thousand   _____

  3 three hundred and fifty   _____

  4 three hundred and fifteen   _____

  5 16   _____

  6 500   _____

  7 105   _____

  8 999   _____

2 **Read. Then circle and write sentences.**

  1 baggy *jumper / trousers* _____

  2 tight *trousers / umbrella* _____

  3 expensive *bracelet / pocket* _____

  4 short *watch / jeans* _____

3 **Read. Then answer.**

  1 Whose leather gloves are these?

    They're (*Harry*) _____ gloves. They're his.

  2 Whose black umbrella is this?

    It's Sandra's umbrella. It's _____ .

  3 Whose silver bracelet is this?

    It's (*Ben*) _____ silver bracelet. It's _____ .

  4 Whose old-fashioned swimsuit is this?

    It's (*you*) _____ swimsuit. It's _____ .

4 **What should you wear to play sports? Make some notes. Then write about it.**

1 **Read. Then write the words.**

1 How much is that gold bracelet?   It's _____ .   (£505)
2 How much are those trousers?   They're _____ .   (£196)
3 How much is the red umbrella?   _____ .   (£37)
4 How much are the black leather gloves?   _____ .   (£83)
5 How much is the old-fashioned hat?   _____ .   (£953)
6 How much are the gold watches?   _____ .   (£1,000)

2 **Read. Then write the questions and answers.**

those baggy / trousers; £60

1 _____

this old-fashioned / wallet; £16

2 _____

that modern / watch; £808

3 _____

this tight / tracksuit; £53

4 _____

3 **Read. Then answer using _his / hers_.**

1 Whose leather belt is this?
   It's Dan's belt. It's _____ .
2 Whose yellow swimsuit is this?
   It's Stella's swimsuit. It's _____ .
3 Whose gold watch is this?
   It's Jamie's watch. It's _____ .
4 Whose modern hat is this?
   It's Bella's hat. It's _____ .

4 **What should you wear to play sports? Make some notes. Then write.**

5 Shopping

1 🔊 4:09 **Listen. Then match.**

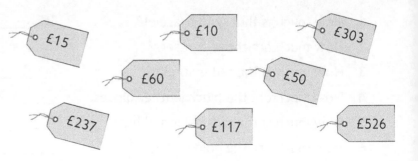

1 jacket

2 leather wallets

3 black and yellow sunglasses

4 spotted umbrella

£15 £10 £303 £60 £50 £237 £117 £526

2 🔊 4:10 **Listen. Then circle.**

1 umbrella	green, brown and white	beautiful	stripes
2 watch	modern	beautiful	old-fashioned
3 shirts	baggy	different coloured	spotted
4 jeans	black	tight	leather pocket

3 **Let's go shopping! What are you going to buy? Write your ideas. Then take turns to be the customer and the shop assistant.**

- How much … ?
- I'm going to save …
- I'll buy …

Customer	
Questions	Answers

Shop assistant	
Questions	Answers

Shopping

1 **Listen. Then complete the table.**

	item	price	colour	material	other comments
1	belt				
2	tracksuit				
3	bracelet				
4	swimsuits				

2 **Listen. Then answer.**

1 What does Judy want to buy?

_____

What is she going to do first?

_____

Which jeans will she buy?

_____

2 What does Ed want to buy?

_____

Why has he got the advertisements?

_____

What is important about the trainers he buys?

_____

How much were the trainers in the adverts?

_____

3 **Let's go shopping! Think of a conversation. Write your ideas. Then talk.**

- How much does it cost?
- This is …
- I'm going to save …
- I'll buy …

Customer:
Shop assistant:
Customer:
Shop assistant:
Customer:
Shop assistant:
Customer:
Shop assistant:

1 Write the numbers.

1 3rd _____

2 15th _____

3 11th _____

4 8th _____

5 5th _____

6 16th _____

7 1st _____

8 13th _____

2 Read. Then match.

1 When did you go on holiday last year?   **a** I went with my parents and my sister.

2 Where did you go on holiday last year?   **b** We went in August.

3 How did you go there?   **c** We saw lots of pyramids.

4 Who did you go with?   **d** No, we couldn't.

5 What did you do?   **e** We went to Mexico.

6 Could you play volleyball?   **f** We took a plane and then went by bus.

3 Read. Then complete. Use *must* or *have to*.

Today we've got a big football game at my club. I [1] _____ go to the club straight after school to get ready for the match. I [2] _____ remember to take my football shorts and shirt. Mum washed them yesterday and I forgot to put them in my school bag this morning. My teacher is coming to watch the game so we [3] _____ play well. She loves football and comes to all our games. In the last game we lost but our teacher said we played really well. This time we [4] _____ win. After the game, my mum and dad are going to take me to a restaurant so I [5] _____ have a shower after the game!

4 What did you do last weekend? Write. Use some of these words.

| bring | give | go | have | listen | make | practise | see | take | watch |

_____

_____

_____

_____

_____

Party time

1 **Write the dates.**

1   2/08   _____

2   15/05   _____

3   14/04   _____

4   18/11   _____

5   5/06   _____

6   9/09   _____

7   1/07   _____

8   12/01   _____

2 **Read the answers. Then write the questions.**

1   _____   I went with my aunt and uncle.

2   _____   We went in July.

3   _____   We played tennis and read books.

4   _____   Yes, we could.

5   _____   We went to the beach in Turkey.

6   _____   We went by boat.

3 **Read and complete. Use *must* or *have to*.**

This afternoon, I ¹ _____ go to my granny's house because it is her birthday.
My mum made her a big cake and she said I ² _____ take it to granny's house
before six o'clock. When I get there, mum said I ³ _____ be very quiet and
put the cake on the kitchen table without granny seeing me. When my mum and dad arrive,
we ⁴ _____ hide behind the kitchen table. We ⁵ _____ keep
very quiet. When my granny comes into the kitchen, we ⁶ _____ jump from
behind the table and sing 'Happy Birthday'!

4 **What did you do two days ago? Write.**

| have   go   see   take   bring   make   practise   give   listen   watch |

_____

_____

_____

_____

_____

1 (4:13) **Listen. Then draw.**

Decorations	Food	Instrument

2 (4:14) **Listen. Then match.**

1 Where did Stef go on holiday?

2 When did he go?

3 What did he do?

4 What did he see?

5 Who did he meet?

6 Where is Stef going next year for his holiday?

h He went to Greece.

f Somewhere cold.

j He saw buildings, guards, statues and fish.

c On the 20th of June.

d On the 28th of June.

a He went to the beach and went to Athens.

e He went swimming every day.

b The UK.

g He saw Greek islands.

i He met one of his teachers.

k He met a school friend.

3 **Think of something special you did last year. Make some notes. Then talk.**

- Was it in autumn / spring … ?
- Was it dangerous / horrible … ?

- I / You have to see / visit / do …
- I / You must …

1 (4:15) **Listen. Then circle _True_ (T) or _False_ (F).**

A

1	There were twenty-five girls at the party.	T / F
2	The garden was too small for the party.	T / F
3	The birthday cake was a chocolate bike.	T / F
4	One present was a gold bracelet.	T / F
5	They all played the piano.	T / F
6	They danced to mum's CDs.	T / F
7	Her friend is ten.	T / F

B

1	His granny is sixty.	T / F
2	Grandad made a barbecue.	T / F
3	There were balloons in the living room.	T / F
4	There were candles on the grass.	T / F
5	Dad couldn't play mini cricket.	T / F
6	Granny wasn't happy.	T / F

2 (4:16) **Listen. Then circle.**

1 Sue went to _Ireland / England_ last year.
2 She went at the beginning of _July / August_.
3 They went _hiking / camping_ in the mountains.
4 Her dad _caught / didn't catch_ a boot.
5 Irish _singing / dancing_ looks very difficult.
6 Ireland is famous for _theatres / storytelling_.

3 **Think of something special you did last year. Make notes. Then talk.**

- Was it in autumn/spring ... ?
- Was it dangerous/horrible ... ?

- I saw/visited/did ...

1 **Read. Then match.**

1 Were you playing tennis yesterday?

2 Was Polly in the gym yesterday morning?

3 Were Janet and Flora shopping this morning?

4 Was Pete excited before his holiday?

a No, she wasn't.

b Yes, I was.

c Yes, he was.

d No, they weren't.

2 **Complete the questions. Then reorder the answers.**

1 How old _____ you? was / old / I / years / four

_____

2 _____ you excited?   I / excited / was / yes / very

_____

3 What _____ the weather like?   was / sunny / it / and / hot / very

_____

4 _____ it interesting?   it / interesting / holiday / a / very / was

_____

3 **Read. Then write *has* or *have*.**

1 I _____ read six books this week.

2 My teacher _____ written a story for a competition on the TV.

3 My friends, Colin and Charles, _____ seen the new film.

4 We _____ learned a lot this year at school.

5 Our English teacher _____ created a new web page on the computer.

6 In Drama, Matt _____ got the biggest part in the school play!

4 **Think of a book or film. Then write about it. Use some of these words.**

| boring   exciting   finished   followed   read   romantic   scary   used |

_____

_____

_____

_____

_____

School

1 Read. Then answer.

1 Were you studying Geography yesterday? ✓ _____ .

2 Was your History teacher ill yesterday morning? ✗ _____ .

3 Were your parents shopping this morning? ✗ _____ .

4 Was the last book you read interesting? ✓ _____ .

5 Were you at school two days ago? ✓ _____ .

6 Was Art your favourite subject last year? ✗ _____ .

2 Write questions. Then reorder the answers.

1 (old) _____ ?

was / three / I / old / years _____ .

2 (excited) _____ ?

wasn't / I / no _____ .

3 (weather like) _____ ?

raining / was / cold / and / it / very _____ .

4 (interesting) _____ ?

No / wasn't / it _____ .

3 Read. Then complete. Use the present perfect.

1 I _____ (read) three books this week.

2 My teacher _____ (write) a story for a writing competition.

3 My friends _____ (see) the latest cartoon film.

4 We _____ (learn) a lot at school.

5 Our PE teacher _____ (create) a new web page on the computer.

6 In Science, Mark _____ (make) the biggest machine ever!

4 What are your favourite and least favourite subjects? Write about them.

boring   difficult   easy   exciting   romantic   scary

_____

_____

_____

_____

_____

1 🔊 4:17 **Listen. Then write. Use the words from the word box.**

> boring exciting History horrible intelligent
> kind plays scary school Science museums

When I was nine, I went to [1] _____ in Argentina. My class had twenty-six
children in it. My class teacher was called Mr Brown. He was a little [2] _____ .
He talked very loudly but he was [3] _____ and funny. My favourite subject was
[4] _____ . Mr Brown gave us lessons in the park. We also had lessons in
[5] _____ and historic buildings. We did short [6] _____ about
some of the history topics. Our parents came to watch us.
But ... Science lessons were [7] _____ . I didn't like the teacher. It wasn't
Mr Brown. The teacher was very [8] _____ but his lessons were a little
[9] _____ . We listened to him talk and talk and we made notes in our books!
I like [10] _____ now. In my new school, we do lots of experiments and that's
fun. But I liked that school. It was [11] _____ going to school in a different country
and everyone was so interesting.

2 🔊 4:18 **Listen. Then write.**

	Monday	Tuesday	Wednesday	Thursday	Friday
morning					
afternoon					

3 **Think about this week. What have you done? Make some notes. Then talk.**

- I've played / made / finished / used / helped ...
- I haven't ...
- I've just ...
- I've already ...

1   **Listen. Then match.**

A

1	History	**a**	exciting
2	Maths	**b**	difficult but not boring
3	Science	**c**	interesting
4	Music	**d**	easy and boring
5	Art	**e**	fun

B

1	field	**a**	trip
2	old	**b**	hundred
3	something	**c**	down
4	bent	**d**	funny
5	silver	**e**	money
6	eight	**f**	buildings

2   **Listen. Then write.**

Index

Chapter		Page #
1 Geography	....	_____
2 L__n____a___	....	3
3 Sc____n__e	....	_____
4 D__c_____n__r y	....	7
5 ____st__r__	....	_____
6 Co__p__t__r S____d____s	....	11

3 **Think about this week. What have you done? Make some notes. Then talk.**

- I've played / made / finished / used / helped / created / went / learned ...
- I've just ...   • I haven't ...   • I've already ...

1 **Read. Then match.**

1	Where are Tom and Sue from?	**a**	I'm from Mexico.
2	Are Jan and Tina Canadian?	**b**	No, I'm Italian.
3	Where are you from?	**c**	They're from Egypt.
4	Is she Polish?	**d**	Yes, they are.
5	Is he from Mexico?	**e**	No, he isn't. He's from Colombia.
6	Are you Argentinian?	**f**	No, she's not. She's Thai.

2 **Read. Then order to make words and match.**

1 I studied Drama. I work in a theatre.

2 I work in a restaurant. I take the food to people.

3 I studied Science. I live in space!

4 I love food! I work with food. I create new dishes for people.

5 I help people. I look after their teeth.

6 I write stories about things that happen. I write for a magazine.

a _____ (soutarant)

b _____ (tsijourlan)

c _____ (tdnesit)

d _____ (kcoo)

e _____ (ratco)

f _____ (rwtaie)

3 **Read. Then circle.**

1 He's a waiter *who / which / where* comes from Brazil.

2 Australia is a big country *who / which / where* there are rainforests.

3 It was a watch *who / which / where* he found in the theatre.

4 She's the girl *which / where / who* teaches me to play the piano.

4 **Write about dates and times. When are they? Then complete.**

1 I played football _____ because I had to visit my cousin on Sunday.

2 The festival of Halloween is _____ .

3 My birthday is _____ .

4 I get up _____ because I have to go to school at 8 o'clock.

5 I usually make my bed _____ .

6 I normally go to bed early but last night I went _____ .

1 **Write the questions.**

1 _____ ?   Yes, I'm from Brazil.

2 _____ ?   No, I'm Spanish.

3 _____ ?   No, they're Egyptian.

4 _____ ?   Yes, they're Canadian.

5 _____ ?   No, he's not. He's Colombian.

6 _____ ?   No, she's not. She's Thai.

2 **Read and order to make words. Then match.**

1 I studied Art. I work in a studio.   (renegeni)

   a _____

2 We take pictures with cameras.   (htpogorapehr)

   b _____

3 I studied Maths and Science. I make houses   (rolaftoble)
   and bridges.
                                                      c _____
4 I practise kicking a ball every day for five hours. (tarsti)
   Every weekend I have a game.   d _____

3 **Read. Then write sentences using _who_, _which_ or _where_.**

1 They are children. They are Chinese.

   _____ .

2 Camels are animals. They are African.

   _____ .

3 This is the library. I found the wallet.

   _____ .

4 This is the shop. I bought my bracelet.

   _____ .

4 **Read the questions. Then answer.**

1 When is your birthday?   _____

2 What time do you get up?   _____

3 When do you not go to school?   _____

4 When do you have breakfast?   _____

5 Which month do you go back to school? _____

6 What year were you five?   _____

7 What time did you go to bed on Saturday? _____

1 (4:21) **Listen. Then write the nationalities.**

1 _ _ _ _ _ _ _
2 _ _ _ _ _ _ _
3 _ _ _ _ _ _ _ _ _
4 _ _ _ _ _ _ _
5 _ _ _ _ _
6 _ _ _ _ _ _

2 (4:22) **Listen. Then find and match.**

football player [ ]   a

journalist [ ]   b

cook [ ]   c

dentist [ ]   d

mechanic [ ]   e

actor [ ]   f

3 **Imagine you are a journalist or football player. Then talk.**

- What time do you start / finish work?
- What do you do in the morning / in spring ... ?
- The place where I work is ...
- That ..., which is ..., is ...

1 **Listen. Then complete.**

Name	Comes from ...	Nationality
1 Pablo		
2 Anton	Krakow	
3 Val		Canadian
4 Ruth	Washington	
5 Marco		
6 Cristobal	Seville	
7 Anna	Beijing	
8 Ryan	Dublin	

2 **Listen. Then circle.**

WHEN WE GROW UP

1	businessman / woman	4 5
2	photographer	3 5
3	actor	8 9
4	dentist	1 6
5	journalist	5 4
6	cook	1
7	mechanic	9 1
8	footballer	2 10
9	engineer	14 4

0 1 2 3 4 5 6 7 8 9 10 11 12 13 14 15 16 17 18

3 **Imagine you are a photographer or a businessman / woman. Draw a mind map or make notes. Then talk.**

- What time do you start / finish work?
- What do you do in the moring / in spring ... ?

- The place where I work is ...
- That ..., which is ..., is ...

End of term 1

1 Read. Then match.

1 What are you good at?

2 Are there any lakes in your country?

3 What do you do at the weekend?

4 What does he look like?

5 What's she like?

6 What do you like doing after school?

7 What was he doing yesterday?

8 Were they watching DVDs?

a I'm good at football.

b He was practising the piano.

c She's very talkative and a little bossy.

d I like meeting my friends.

e No, they weren't.

f He's tall and he's got short brown hair.

g Yes, there are.

h I play volleyball with my friends.

2 Read and look. Then answer.

1 What were you doing last night?

2 What are you good at?

3 What does she look like?

4 What's she like?

5 What is she doing?

6 How often should you brush your teeth?

3 **Read the questions. Then order the answers.**

1 What were you doing yesterday evening?   was / tennis / playing / I

_____

2 What sports are you good at?   am / at / good / I / football / basketball / and

_____

3 Are you good at playing a musical instrument?   not / I'm / no

_____

4 What are you like?   am / sporty / and / I / kind

_____

5 What does your best friend look like?   got / she's / straight / blonde / hair

_____

6 What do you love doing?   love / I / rollerblading / trampolining / and

_____

4 **Read. Then sort the words. Add your own.**

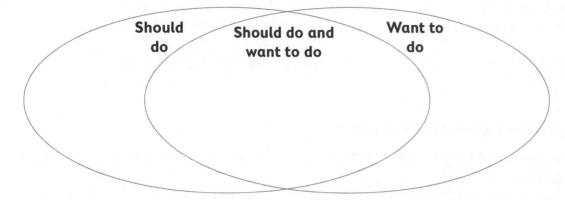

Should
do

Should do and
want to do

Want to
do

brush my teeth   wash my face   do my homework   take out the rubbish tidy my bedroom
set the table   go shopping   read books   practise the piano   play in a band   play video games

5 **Write about you and your teachers.**

- What do you like doing?
- I'm good at ...

- I play / practise / go ... in the park / stadium ...
- My teacher plays ...

_____

_____

_____

_____

1 Read. Then match.

1 Are there any deserts in your country?

2 How much is this bracelet?

3 Whose gloves are these?

4 When was her mum's birthday?

5 When did you go to Turkey?

6 Is this her helmet?

7 Are there any cheap sunglasses?

8 Is there a statue in your town?

a It was last week.

b No, there aren't.

c Yes there is. It's in the town centre.

d No, it isn't. It's mine.

e It's very expensive. It's £500.

f They're my mum's.

g We went last year.

h Yes, there are. Here. These aren't expensive.

2 Order to make questions. Then match.

1 volcanoes / are / any / there / country / your / in

_____

2 a / is / there / mountains / cave / the / in

_____

3 jacket / how / the / much / is

_____

4 this / whose / wallet / is / brown

_____

5 won / swimming / the / who / competition

_____

6 very / those / tight / trousers / are

_____

a Yes, and the shirt is very baggy!

b Number three hundred and five.

c It's sixty-five pounds.

d It's my dad's.

e Yes, there is a cave in the mountains.

f Yes. There are three.

3 **Read the questions. Then order and write the answers.**

1 Is there a rainforest in your country? there / is / no / not

_____ .

2 Are there any pyramids in Mexico? there / are / yes / are / there / lots

_____ .

3 What do you usually bring to a birthday party? bring /a / I / present / usually

_____ .

4 Whose book is this? it's / book / Les'

_____ .

5 When is your birthday? my / is / on / birthday / the / of / May / 1st

_____ .

6 When did you go shopping with your friends? went / two / I / shopping / ago / days

_____ .

4 **Read and sort the words. Then write sentences.**

gloves	**clothes**	**adjectives**	old-fashioned
bracelet			sunglasses
helmet			expensive
swimsuit			baggy
cheap			tight

_____ .

_____ .

_____ .

_____ .

5 **Your ideal summer. Write about it.**

- When was your holiday?
- It was on / in / a ...

- I went to ...
- I ... (activity)

_____

_____

_____

_____

_____

1 **Read. Then match.**

1 Were you in the competition?

2 Where was the winner from?

3 Did they visit Korea?

4 Was it difficult?

5 Were there any cowboys in the film?

6 Is she the girl who's in the play?

7 Are they American?

8 Was your friend in the play?

a Yes, they did.

b No, she wasn't.

c No, it wasn't. It was easy.

d Yes, I was.

e No, they aren't. They're Australian.

f She was from Greece.

g Yes, she is.

h Yes, there were.

2 **Read the questions. Then order and write the answers.**

1 Was the film interesting?   scary / yes / but / was / it

_____ .

2 Where are they from?   they / Egyptian / are / both

_____ .

3 Were there any aliens in the film   lots / there / yes / were

_____ .

4 Were there any firefighters in the film?   there / no / three / but / were / sailors

_____ .

5 Was the Science lesson interesting?   tests / with / yes / did / some / exciting / water / we / and / salt

_____ .

6 What time did they go to bed?   the / morning / at / quarter / to / four / in

_____ .

3 **Order to make questions.**

1 from / your / teacher / where's

_____ ?

2 you / last / America / did / year / visit

_____ ?

3 TV / film / watch / did / last / you / a / on / week

_____ ?

4 the / scary / was / film

_____ ?

5 year / competition / school / in / were / a / you / last

_____ ?

6 did / Tuesday / have / Maths / on / you

_____ ?

4 **Read and match. Then write sentences.**

1 Geo		**e** sy		**5** Sci		**g** tory	
2 Ma		**a** ring		**6** diff		**d** ence	
3 ea		**b** ths		**7** His		**c** esting	
4 bo		**h** graphy		**8** inter		**f** icult	

_____

_____

_____

_____

5 **Write about a famous person that you like.**

- He / She is from ...
- He / She is (nationality)
- He / She is a(n) ...
- He / She likes ...

_____

_____

_____

_____

_____

_____

_____

_____

 Read. Then circle.

MY SCHOOL NEWS

VOL. **1**, NO. **2**   BARCELONA, SPAIN   TODAY'S DATE

END OF TERM PARTY!

This year at school we had an end of term party. We haven't had a party before. Every class had a job to do. My class had to bring the food and drinks. I made a fruit cake and a carrot cake. They were very tasty. My best friend, Sarah, made a mushroom and spinach pizza and some egg sandwiches. I took some salt and pepper and some sugar.

On the day, we were very excited. We listened to CDs and we had some competitions. I came second in the karaoke competition! Julia, who is in the class above mine, came first.

After singing we had some food. We ate and ate. There was a lot of food. There wasn't much fruit! The food was really quite unhealthy ... but it was lovely.

Then we danced. It was an excellent day. Everyone was so helpful and everyone really had a lot of fun. But the next day ... oh, what a mess!

1 The school had an end of year party ...

   a every year.

   b sometimes.

   c this year.

2 Sarah ...

   a didn't make a cake.

   b brought some salt and pepper.

   c won a competition.

3 After the party ...

   a we didn't tidy up.

   b we danced.

   c we had a lot of fun.

4 Every class ...

   a made a cake.

   b helped.

   c sang.

5 The food ...

   a was very healthy.

   b wasn't very good for us.

   c wasn't very nice.

1 **Read. Then write *True* (T) or *False* (F).**

JGD SCHOOL NEWS

VOL. 2, NO. 5 BARCELONA, SPAIN TODAY'S DATE

Hi. I'm Maria. I live in England and I'm English. My cousin is here at the moment. He's from Ireland. His name is Sean. That's an Irish name. They don't say *Seeyan*, they say *Shorn*. Some people in Ireland speak Irish. It's very different to English.

Sean is going to school with me. He's going to sit next to me in class and he's going to be in all my lessons. It's so exciting.

Last night, we watched DVDs until midnight! It was Friday and mum and dad said it was ok. They made us a pizza and gave us some fruit juice and then they went to bed at 10.30 p.m.

This morning we were very tired. We had breakfast at 11 a.m! Then we played cricket in the garden. Dad taught me how to play last year – it was quite difficult to understand at first but now it's easy. And Sean can play, too. My uncle taught him.

After lunch, we went shopping. I got some trainers. They were £20. That's quite cheap! Sean got a wallet that cost £30. That's quite expensive! I hope he doesn't forget his wallet because tomorrow we're going to the cinema!

Well … I should get ready. I've got a football game at 5 o'clock and it's now half past four!

1 Sean is staying in Ireland. ☐

2 Maria doesn't want Sean to go to school with her. ☐

3 Sean and Maria went to bed after mum and dad. ☐

4 They got a pizza from the pizza restaurant. ☐

5 Maria's dad taught Maria and Sean to play cricket. ☐

6 Sean got a new wallet which was expensive. ☐

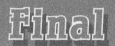

1 Read. Then complete.

| am   are   in   love   played   singing   snowboarding   went |

Last winter, I [1] _____ to the mountains with my family. We [2] _____

skiing. My mum and dad [3] _____ good at skiing. I [4] _____ not

good at skiing but I am good at [5] _____ . [6] _____ the evenings,

my dad [7] _____ the guitar and we sang. We love [8] _____ .

2 Write the numbers.

1 300 _____

2 278 _____

3 659 _____

4 114 _____

3 Write the questions.

1 _____ ?

Yes, I'm Egyptian.

2 _____ ?

I went to Turkey.

3 _____ ?

They are good at skiing.

4 _____ ?

Yes, it was very interesting.

4 Write *in*, *on* or *at*.

I'm British and I live in Manchester. My favourite hobby is acting. [1] _____

spring, I go to acting club [2] _____ Thursdays. It's [3] _____

five o'clock after school. It's great fun! I was in a competition [4] _____

May and I was the winner! Now I want to be an actress. I'm excited because there's a

school summer camp [5] _____ August and there are acting classes!

5 Order to make sentences. Then match.

1 you / Why / excited / ? / are

_____

a to / went /I / Ibiza.

_____

2 often / your / How / ? / do / you / tidy / room

_____

b tomorrow / my / 's / birthday / Because.

_____

3 last / you / Where / did / ? / summer / go

_____

c midday / Every / at/ Saturday.

_____

1 **Read. Then complete with the verb in the correct form.**

> come   eat   get   give   have   help   play   sing

Yesterday was Jo's birthday. She is eleven now. She ¹ _____ a new bike.

Sue ² _____ Jo a new bag as a present. Jo ³ _____

a party. It was fun. Everyone ⁴ _____ 'Happy Birthday'. Jo's cousins

⁵ _____ to the party. They ⁶ _____ some games in

the garden. They ⁷ _____ pizza and birthday cake after the games. Jo

⁸ _____ her mum to make the cake.

2 **Write the questions.**

1 _____ ? Yes, I'm Egyptian.

2 _____ ? I went to Turkey.

3 _____ ? They are good at skiing.

4 _____ ? This book is mine.

5 _____ ? She came home last weekend.

6 _____ ? No, I didn't watch the TV last night.

3 **Order to make sentences.**

1 your / any / in / are / country / mountains / there

_____?

2 in / family / she / the / is / her / tallest

_____.

3 doctor / go / should / you / the / to

_____.

4 party / come / he / couldn't / the / to

_____.

5 **Read. Then complete.**

> chocolate   score   storyboards   snack   scissors   midday
> characters   glue   sang   birthday

Yesterday was my ¹ _____ and I had a party. All my friends came. It was

great! First we made ² _____ using ³ _____ and

⁴ _____. We invented funny ⁵ _____! Then, at

⁶ _____, we had a ⁷ _____. There were plates of

⁸ _____ biscuits, my favourite! Finally we ⁹ _____

karaoke and my cousin got the highest ¹⁰ _____. It was really fun!

1 (4:25) **Listen. Then complete.**

Yesterday I ¹ *watched / went* my brother play ² *football / basketball*. It ³ *was / were* very exciting. The game was very ⁴ *difficult / different*. He ⁵ *practised / studied* for weeks. I ⁶ *went / go* with my mum and dad. It finished at ⁷ *a quarter past eleven / half past ten*. We got home ⁸ *at / on* midday. My brother was very ⁹ *tired / thirsty*. He didn't do his homework! He ¹⁰ *listened to / watched* TV. I ¹¹ *played / chatted* to my friends. I was ¹² *telling / talking* them funny jokes.

2 (4:26) **Listen. Then write.**

	Where from	Activity	When	Where
Sue				
Tony				

3 (4:27) **Listen. Then match.**

expensive

baggy

lovely

old-fashioned

tight

cheap

4 (4:28) **Listen. Then number.**

My new DVD	
funny	☐
scary	☐
boring	☐
exciting	☐

1 (4:29) **Listen. Then complete.**

> watched   exciting   difficult   violin   practised   went   finished   midnight
> didn't do   must   met   Mexican

Yesterday I [1] _____ my dad play the [2] _____ in a
concert. It was very [3] _____ . The music was very [4] _____ .
He [5] _____ for weeks. I [6] _____ with my mum and
sister. It [7] _____ at half past ten. We got home at [8] _____ .
I was very tired. I [9] _____ my homework! I [10] _____ do it
today. I [11] _____ some of my dad's friends. We went for dinner in a
[12] _____ restaurant.

2 (4:30) **Listen. Then write.**

	Where from	Activity	When	Where
Stephanie				
Rob				

3 (4:31) **Listen. Then match.**

1 Spanish	label	bracelet
2 Australian	expensive	umbrella
3 Brazilian	baggy	candle
4 Italian	mechanic	helmet
5 Turkish	cheap	trousers
6 Argentinian	birthday present	belt

4 (4:32) **Listen. Then number.**

Competitions	
• karaoke competition	☐
• drum-playing competition	☐
• chess competition	☐
• poetry reading competition	☐
• joke-telling competition	☐

1 Find the differences.

1

2

1 **Tell the story. What happened?**

1 **Look and read. Then match.**

1	Some people have this so they aren't cold.	**a**	Greek
2	A person who comes from Greece.	**b**	scarf
3	A bird has got these.	**c**	Maths
4	A lesson at school which has number questions.	**d**	umbrella
5	You want this when it's rainy.	**e**	midday
6	The word for the middle of the day.	**f**	wings

2 **Look and read. Write *Yes* or *No*.**

1 There is a girl with long hair and a bag.   _____

2 There is a girl throwing a ball.   _____

3 There aren't any cats in the picture.   _____

4 A boy is kicking a ball.   _____

5 There are two boys wearing white t-shirts.   _____

6 There is a boy with a small dog.   _____

3 Tim is talking to his mum. What does his mum say? Read and write a, b or c for each answer.

    a Okay. Well ... what about chicken and spinach?

    b We've got chicken and broccoli.

    c Broccoli is good for you. It's very healthy.

    1 **Tim**: Hi, Mum. What's for dinner?

        Mum: ☐

    2 **Tim**: Ugh. Broccoli? I don't like broccoli.

        Mum: ☐

    3 **Tim**: Oh, ... but Mum, I don't like healthy food.

        Mum: ☐

        Tim: Oh, Muuuuumm!!

4 Read the story. Then complete.

> climbed   got   had   made   started   walked   was   weren't

Yesterday we went for a walk in the mountains. We [1] _____ for six hours.

It was a very long day. It [2] _____ very sunny in the morning but by midday

it was very cloudy. We [3] _____ up a big mountain. It was hard work and I

was very tired. We [4] _____ lunch at the top.

In the afternoon, it [5] _____ to rain. We [6] _____

happy. I had my umbrella in my rucksack. We [7] _____ back at six o'clock.

Mum [8] _____ a nice drink of hot chocolate!

5 Read. Then answer.

Spain is a very interesting country. If you go to the cities you can see lots of statues. If you go
to the Spanish islands you can find caves and in some of them there are volcanoes.
In the area known as Galicia there are lovely lakes and forests. There's also a desert called
Monegros. Come and visit Spain!

    1 Are there any deserts in Spain?

    _____.

    2 What can you find in the cities?

    _____.

    3 Where are the volcanoes?

    _____.

    4 Are there any pyramids?

    _____.

1 **Listen. Then draw lines.**

Harry   James   Frankie   Nick   Clara   Susie

2 **Listen. Then write.**

MONDAY

1

TUESDAY

2

WEDNESDAY

3

THURSDAY

4

FRIDAY

5

SATURDAY

6

3 **Listen. Then number.**

Where did Bill's friends go on holiday?

a 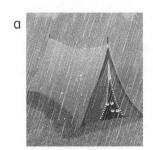 b 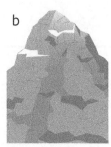 c  d

Bob ☐ Mandy ☐ David ☐ Angela ☐

4 **Listen. Then tick (✓).**

a  ☐ b  ☐ c  ☐ d  ☐

e  ☐ f  ☐ g  ☐ h  ☐

Listen. Then colour and draw.

1 **Read. Then match.**

1	We wear this when we go swimming.	**a**	Geography
2	A person who comes from Ireland.	**b**	midnight
3	An artist does this.	**c**	jacket
4	We learn about volcanoes in this lesson.	**d**	Irish
5	You want this when it's cold.	**e**	paint
6	The word for the middle of the night.	**f**	swimsuit
7	There are twelve of these in a year.	**g**	digestion
8	How the body processes food you eat.	**h**	months

2 **Look and read. Write *Yes* or *No*.**

1 The girl with long hair has got a big hat. _____

2 The boy behind the girl with the hat is jumping. _____

3 There are two dogs in the picture. _____

4 Two boys are playing badminton. _____

5 The boy with the white t-shirt is catching a ball. _____

6 The girl with the dog is wearing a spotty skirt. _____

7 There are two girls wearing hats. _____

8 The boy who is running looks very tired. _____

3 **Kate is talking to her friend, Sue. What does Sue say?**

Read the conversation and choose the best answer. Write a, b or c for each answer.

a   Okay. I'll meet you by the classroom door at 4 p.m.

b   Not really. I went last night.

c   That's a good idea. I need some new trousers.

1 **Kate**: Hi Sue. Do you want to go to the cinema this evening?

   Sue: _____

2 **Kate**: Oh. Well, what about going shopping?

   Sue: _____

3 **Kate**: Let's go after school.

   Sue: _____

4 **Read the story. Then complete.**

came   didn't   finished   had   made   started   was   were

Yesterday we ¹ _____ a chess competition at school. We had children

from Spain, China, Colombia ... . There ² _____ over five hundred

children. The children ³ _____ with their teachers. The competition

⁴ _____ on Monday and ⁵ _____ on the Friday. On

Saturday, there ⁶ _____ a big party for all the children in the competition.

My school always does well but this year we ⁷ _____ . We need to practise

more! But that's okay. We had fun and ⁸ _____ a lot of new friends.

5 **Read. Then write *True* (T) or *False* (F).**

I like shopping. Usually I go to a department store to buy my clothes.
Last week I wanted to buy a tracksuit and some trainers to run races at school. I asked the
shop assistant to help me, but the tracksuits were too expensive so I decided to go to a
charity shop because I saw an advertisement in a magazine.
The clothes were cheaper than in the department store.
When I got my change I had enough money to buy a new bracelet!

1   The shop assistant helped her.   _____

2   She bought the tracksuit at the department store.   _____

3   The charity shop was cheaper than the department store.   _____

4   She didn't have enough money to buy a bracelet.   _____

1   **Listen. Then draw lines.**

Michael   Jack   Tony   Vicky   Cynthia   Helen

2   **Listen. Then write.**

LOST ITEM REPORT

1 Name: _____

2 Address: _____North Street, Little Troddick_____

3 What's been lost? _____

4 What's inside? _____

5 Where last had it? _____

6 Contact number: _____

3 (4:40) **Listen. Then write a letter in each box. Where did Alex leave his things?**

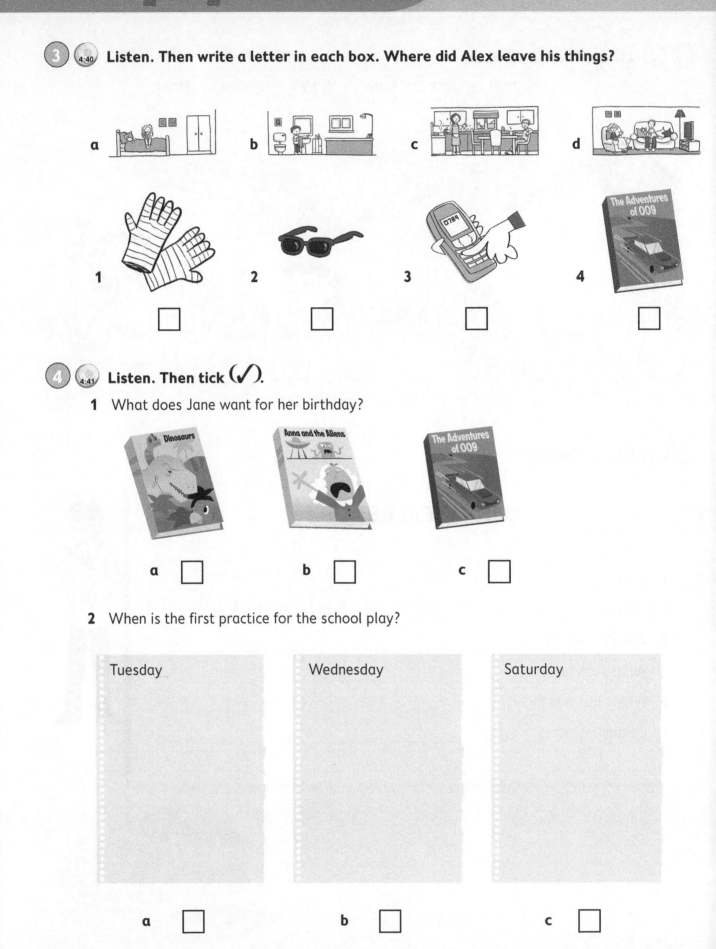

a   b   c   d

1   ☐   2   ☐   3   ☐   4   ☐

4 (4:41) **Listen. Then tick (✓).**

1 What does Jane want for her birthday?

a ☐   b ☐   c ☐

2 When is the first practice for the school play?

Tuesday	Wednesday	Saturday

a ☐   b ☐   c ☐

5 **Listen. Then colour and draw.**

1 Find five differences.

1

2

1 What are your favourite books and films? Draw a mind map. Then talk.

Favourite books and films
Who are the characters?
Was it *funny / scary / exciting* ... ?
What differences are there
between the book and film?

2 Ask and answer questions.

- What would you like to be? Why?
- What wouldn't you like to be? Why?
- What do you think you would study?

Pearson Education Limited
Edinburgh Gate
Harlow
Essex CM20 2JE
England
and Associated Companies throughout the world.

www.islands.pearson.com

© Pearson Education Limited 2012

Written by Kerry Powell

First published 2012
Third Impression 2015
ISBN: 978-1-4082-9075-0

Printed in Great Britain by Ashford Colour Press Ltd

Picture Credits
The publisher would like to thank the following for their kind
permission to reproduce their photographs:
(Key: b-bottom; c-centre; l-left; r-right; t-top)

Alamy Images: Aurora Photos 13b, Ian Cranham 55 (f),
The Photolibrary Wales 55 (d), Colin Underhill 55 (h);
Getty Images: J S Sira / Garden Picture Library 12;
Shutterstock.com: Artpose Adam Borkowski 55 (Bob),
Tomasz Trojanowski 13, 55 (Mandy), Tracy Whiteside 55
(Angela), WilleeCole 55 (David), Peter Zurek 55 (b)

All other images © Pearson Education

All illustrative artworks © Pearson Education Limited 2012

ISBN 978-1-4082-9075-0

9 781408 290750 >